When the buds are blossoming

(Ruddigore)

4

6

The world is but a broken toy
(Princess Ida)

Original key B major

Try we life-long

(The Gondoliers)

Original: S.A.T.Bar.B.

Strange the views some people hold

(The Grand Duke)

Each is laid in church-yard mould— strange the views some peo-ple hold,
If so-ci-e-ty were poll'd, who'd sup-pose the me-thod old,

strange the views _____ some peo-ple hold, strange, strange,
strange the views, strange the views some peo-ple hold,
strange the views, strange the views some peo-ple hold,
strange the views, strange the views some peo-ple hold,
strange the views, strange the views some peo-ple hold,

A nice dilemma

(Trial by Jury)

Hail Poetry

(The Pirates of Penzanze)

Choral Programme Series

Choral repertoire builders with a difference!

Each volume in this brand-new series offers 20–30 minutes of choral music, designed to assist all SATB choirs, large and small, amateur and professional, in imaginative concert programming. Repertoire is drawn from the 18th, 19th and 20th centuries, as well as new commissions, with the emphasis on unavailable, unpublished or unknown material. With expert guidance from Consultant Editor Simon Halsey, maximum practicality is ensured, making the *Choral Programme Series* an invaluable addition to SATB concert repertoire.

Imaginative, versatile and great value for money!

The Choral Programme Series:

Gilbert & Sullivan – Opera Choruses 1
SATB/keyboard. Edited by Ronald Corp

Eagle high in cloudland soaring (*Utopia Limited*)
Strange adventure (*The Yeomen of the Guard*)
Brightly dawns our wedding day (*The Mikado*)
Tho' p'raps I may incur your blame (*Iolanthe*)
I rejoice that it's decided (*The Sorcerer*)
I hear the soft note (*Patience*)

Gilbert & Sullivan – Opera Choruses 2
SATB/keyboard. Edited by Ronald Corp

When the buds are blossoming (*Ruddigore*)
The world is but a broken toy (*Princess Ida*)
Try we life-long (*The Gondoliers*)
Strange the views some people hold
(*The Grand Duke*)
A nice dilemma (*Trial by Jury*)
Hail Poetry (*The Pirates of Penzance*)

Franz Schubert – Four Partsongs
SATB/keyboard. Edited by Judith Blezzard

Lebenslust
An die Sonne
Schicksalslenker
Der Tanz

C.V. Stanford – Seven Partsongs
SATB

Diaphenia
Corydon, arise!
Shall we go dance?
When Mary thro' the garden went
The blue bird
The haven
Chillingham

Five English Folksongs
SATB. Arranged by Daryl Runswick

Dance to thy daddy
She moved through the fair
The frog and the crow
Scarborough Fair
Bobby Shaftoe

Five American Folksongs
SATB. Arranged by Daryl Runswick

Yankee Doodle
Shenandoah
Shortnin' bread – Pick a bale o' cotton
The streets of Laredo
Frog went a-courtin'

Faber Music 3 Queen Square London WC1N 3AU

ISBN 0-571-51196-1

9 780571 511969